Stories of Mothers Lost

Created by the White Ribbon Alliance

In the spirit of the White Ribbon Alliance's
support for mothers and newborns, a donation
from the proceeds of this book will be made to
the White Ribbon Alliance

1 3 5 7 9 10 8 6 4 2

First published in the United Kingdom in 2008
by White Ribbon Alliance Books

White Ribbon Alliance
CAN Mezzanine
32–36 Loman Street
London SE1 OEH

Commissioning Editor: Theresa Shaver

Edited by Brigid McConville, John Shearlaw,
Catharine Taylor and Tamara Windau

Designed by Matt Bucknall

Photographic reproduction by
Prudence Cuming Associates Ltd

Stories of Mothers Lost was made possible by a
grant from the United Nations Population Fund

A CIP catalogue record is available for this book
from the British Library

ISBN: 978 0 9558758 0 9

Printed in the United Kingdom
at the University Press, Cambridge

Cover image: For Delfina from the Safe Birth
and Motherhood Committee of Bolivia

Contents

Reducing the shame of 1 in 8
A Foreword by Sarah Brown

One death per minute

The year is 2008. We live in a fast changing sophisticated world with our global communications, easy travel and 24-hour news services. We are all used to feeling strongly about poverty, the environment and world security. Most of us do what we can to support different charities, get involved with local organisations and have a concern for what happens around the globe. Some of us are able to exercise our passion for great causes. We work hard to raise our own children and we believe we are good world citizens. You name it, we play our part.

And yet think of this... In 2008, at least 1 in 8 women have a lifetime risk of dying in pregnancy and childbirth in the poorest and most conflict torn countries in the world, such as Sierra Leone and Afghanistan. That's right, 1 in 8 in 2008. Half a million mothers' lives will be lost between now and this time next year. Think about it – that is one death every minute. Across sub-Saharan Africa and much of south Asia, mothers are dying needlessly at the time when they are bringing new life into the world. Heartbreakingly, 80 per cent of these deaths are easily avoidable, which is why it's vital that we move fast to start reducing them.

We have the knowledge to change this

Twenty years ago the world came together in the Safe Motherhood Initiative, launched by the World Health Organisation and partners, to reduce the rates of maternal death and illness. Yet, two decades on, and half-way to the 2015 target date of the Millennium Development Goals, United Nations Secretary General Ban Ki-Moon has announced that no overall progress has been made – especially on Millennium Development Goal number 5, which is to improve maternal health. This is the goal where we have made least progress of all. This year, last year and each year until we get our act together, nearly half of the world's women will give birth alone or with only an untrained neighbour or relative to help them. But here's the thing... it's no longer an issue of knowledge, we now *know* how to save these lives, it's an issue of advocacy and will.

What gives us hope is that this is a problem *with* a solution. We have the knowledge to change this. We need to call on global leaders to improve the healthcare systems in countries where maternal and infant mortality is high. We need to call for greater numbers of skilled healthcare providers – whether they be doctors, nurses or midwives – to be present for antenatal care and at the time of birth and soon after. In all countries, not just those in the West, a good functioning healthcare system is needed that works with women in their communities to bring better nutrition, better children's health, and better ante and postnatal care.

All we need is the will

In October 2007, at the Women Deliver conference in London and the White Ribbon Alliance gathering that followed at Downing Street, we saw an attempt to change these appalling statistics. I believe that the time has come where this commitment will translate into action and results, which is why the work the White Ribbon Alliance for Safe Motherhood is doing in over 90 countries around the world is so important. This global advocacy group is providing a powerful voice for mothers everywhere.

Its members include the vast majority of significant governmental and non-governmental organisations – both national and international, many smaller community groups, plus dedicated individuals from all walks of life and countries with high maternal mortality. Working from the grassroots up, the White Ribbon Alliance finds ways to reach women living in communities where they are vulnerable in pregnancy and childbirth. It is these local connections that provide vital information on maternal deaths in each country. They bring massive experience and understanding directly to mothers who face such vast challenges trying to do exactly what should be a natural right – to bear and raise a family.

The White Ribbon Alliance calls on every woman – and man – who has the opportunity to make a difference to take action immediately to right the shameful wrong of the maternal mortality figures. Each of us can be an effective advocate for an issue about which there is often silence, and which sometimes embarrasses men in positions of power. Each of us can tackle this issue by speaking out effectively and often; each of us can support mothers around the world by joining the White Ribbon Alliance.

It works

The best indicator of how a health system is functioning in a country is its maternal mortality ratio; it is painfully clear that strengthening the healthcare systems in each country is the answer. I have visited so many maternal health centres where I've seen overstretched services with committed teams and insufficient equipment. Even basic supplies, such as painkillers, are often missing. For too many women, something as simple as thread for stitches has been the difference between survival and death.

The call by the White Ribbon Alliance for greater women's empowerment is absolutely right and here's why... In southern India where women are empowered within their communities, unsurprisingly, you see a corresponding drop in maternal mortality as well as better survival rates for newborns. Here too, girls stay in school longer and postpone starting their own families. Putting an emphasis on women's rights, and in particular the rights of girls to stay on in school, is key. You can also see the difference in those African countries where women are demanding a greater involvement with political action, coupled with greater investment and expenditure on health. The difference is simple; when fewer women die in childbirth, fewer children die before their fifth birthday, and the country's economy directly benefits. It's win win.

Women are the key

Many of the same women invited to the launch of the Safe Motherhood Initiative 20 years ago are still involved today, and we have their expertise to draw on. The White Ribbon Alliance grows ever stronger as a movement determined to bring about change through its *Promise to Mothers Lost* campaign, which will follow global leaders around the world calling for an urgent response. The stunning fabric panels of the *Stories of Mothers Lost* collection, as gathered in this book, have already been exhibited at Downing Street in London and now travel to major cities where global leaders meet together. Each panel is lovingly and beautifully designed, made by communities from many different countries around the world. Each piece conveys the haunting sadness of a mother's death in childbirth.

The other Millennium Development Goals will not be achieved without mothers. For instance, more than one third of child deaths and 11 per cent of the total disease burden worldwide are due to maternal and child malnutrition. We want our mothers to survive for their own sake, and so that all our children have the best chances in life. Every time a mother survives pregnancy and childbirth, her child's life chances improve – especially if the child is a girl. Yet it is the Millennium Development Goal number 5 – to reduce maternal mortality – that has made the least progress of them all and is also the least spoken about. We need to place this forgotten Millennium Development Goal at the top of the 2008 agenda and reduce the shame of 1 in 8.

Sarah Brown
Patron of White Ribbon Alliance
April 2008

The story of
Stories of Mothers Lost

It is very rare for the stories of poor women from developing countries to be heard in the wider, more prosperous world. Rarer still when death has silenced them.

This is one of the reasons why not much has changed for nearly half of the world's women who still give birth alone, or at home with only friends and neighbours to help them. From our perspective in wealthier countries where many women want a home birth, that can sound almost enviable – but when things go wrong we know that an ambulance is just minutes away.

For pregnant women who cannot get to a health centre – because of distance, poverty, traditional beliefs or lack of freedom to make that choice – when things go wrong it can mean terror, agony and ultimately death.

This book breaks the long silence around maternal death and makes known the stories of those who died, together with the thoughts and feelings of those who are left behind missing them. Of course, these stories are deeply sad, but they also reveal the strength, courage and determination of communities to put an end to this dreadful and wholly preventable injustice.

The initiative to gather these stories began in 2007 when the White Ribbon Alliance, with funding from the United Nations Population Fund, sent out a call to our thousands of members across the world. Would they make a fabric panel to commemorate a woman in their community who had died in pregnancy or childbirth? The response was overwhelming. Over 120 panels from 46 organisations, representing women from 19 countries across four continents, were sent to us at the Royal College of Obstetricians and Gynaecologists in London, whose International Office generously offered space and hosted our exhibition.

We unwrapped them in amazement, each one a work of art and a heart-stopping sombre tale. Suddenly, in this elegant building next to London's Regent's Park, the truth of women's lives and needless deaths became manifest in our hands. The impact was immediate, visceral and unforgettable. The exhibition, launched on October 16th, 2007, at the Royal College of Obstetricians and Gynaecologists moved hearts and minds. During 2008 the exhibition of panels travelled around the world with funding from the Bill and Melinda Gates Foundation.

But what you see on these pages is only part of the global picture. What you do not see are the inspiring activities of the communities who made these panels, how they insisted that the women and girls they loved should not be forgotten – and above all, how they continue to strive for a safer, fairer world for the women of the future. Efforts by the Mahatma Gandhi Institute of Medical Sciences in India moved a husband to bring out the precious photograph of his lost wife, to share his memories of her with his community. Members of this community set up an emergency transport network so that no more women need die in agony by the side of the road; young men and women took oaths that no more of their friends, sisters, neighbours or loved ones should lose their lives in bringing new life into the world.

The work of the White Ribbon Alliance members has been powerful not only in their own families, villages and communities – but it has changed minds and policies in the countries where these mothers lived. The Blue Veins organisation of Pakistan took their story to, and these were published in, 24 different newspapers across the country. The Women's Information Network of Enugu State in Nigeria convinced two leading newspapers to campaign against the high cost of antenatal services for women – and the government took notice. In December 2007, antenatal services were made free of charge to all women across the State of Enugu.

White Ribbon Alliance members around the world continue to work for change. They are putting pressure on their governments, local and national, holding them accountable for the health services they should provide for women. Meetings between villagers, health professionals, politicians, young people and religious leaders are going on as you read this. People across Africa, Asia and Latin America are marching to demonstrate their solidarity and press for change. Television and radio stations, newspapers and magazines are taking notice and spreading the word that this movement is rapidly gathering force.

In this book you can see one highly creative expression of what is now a powerful global movement, with its roots in villages, town and cities across the developing world. Men and women from all walks of life are working tirelessly to end the shame of needless maternal death. Join us; we can accomplish even more together.

Theresa Shaver
President / Executive Director
White Ribbon Alliance Global Secretariat

Brigid McConville, Catharine Taylor
White Ribbon Alliance Board of Directors

Afghanistan

Zarmnia

From the Afghan Midwives Association

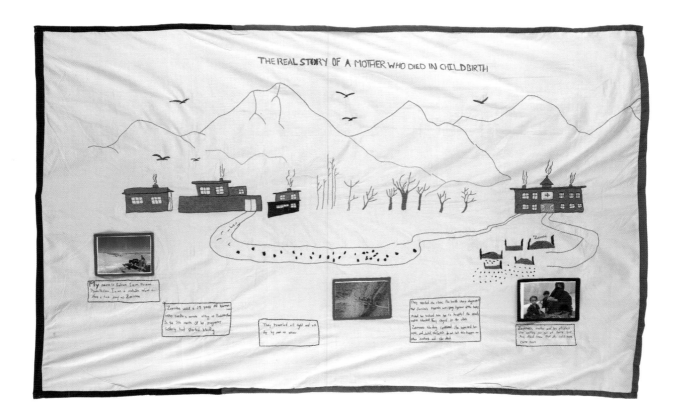

Bangladesh

Shefali Akhtar

Shefali had two children, aged eight and five and she was pregnant for the third time. She was a religious, conservative individual who had never received any vaccinations or antenatal care during her previous healthy pregnancies. During this pregnancy too Shefali's appetite was normal and her health was relatively good. She occasionally suffered from headaches, and when she was six months pregnant she developed night blindness, but she never consulted a doctor or faith healer.

After nine months, Shefali's labour pains started at seven o'clock one evening. She called her mother, who was a traditional birth attendant, to come to her house. After she had finished her prayers at nine o'clock, her labour pains increased. Around one o'clock in the morning, Shefali's waters broke and her baby was safely born.

Shortly after the birth however, Shefali felt dizzy. Her mother-in-law and sister-in-law were washing the baby when Shefali said she felt sick and complained of a severe headache. Her sister-in-law helped her to sit on the bed and Shefali started to bleed.

Her husband tried to fetch a doctor but the doctor would not come until the morning. After an hour of heavy bleeding, Shefali's whole body became cold and pale. Her bleeding finally began to slow and she was given a hot compress. Then Shefali began to tremble and clench her teeth. After half an hour she was exhausted, lying on the bed with her eyes closed. At five o'clock in the morning she died.

Shefali was 38 years old, and her preventable death left behind three children to continue their lives without their mother.

From the White Ribbon Alliance for Safe Motherhood Bangladesh & MotherNewBorNet

Fatema Begum

Fatema was married at 14 and pregnant at 18. After five months of pregnancy, she experienced pain and bleeding. Her baby had died inside her. Fatema's in-laws blamed evil spirits and called a faith healer. The pain lessened after drinking his holy water, but she developed a high fever. The healer shaved off Fatema's hair and applied traditional medication to her head. After great pain and suffering lasting a week, her dead baby still inside her, Fatema died.

From the White Ribbon Alliance for Safe Motherhood Bangladesh & MotherNewBorNet

Julekha Begum

Julekha was 18. She had been unhappily married for three years and was five months pregnant at the time of her death. Here is her story, told from two very different sides.

This is what her in-laws said:
Julekha was well the day before her death. She woke up and did housework as usual. At six o'clock in the morning her husband and mother-in-law went to a neighbour's house and she was left at home alone. At eight o'clock however, her mother-in-law returned home and found Julekha dead. She told Julekha's parents and then the police. The police took her body away to carry out a post-mortem and reported that Julekha had died from high blood pressure.

This is what her family and neighbours said:
Julekha's mother-in-law had tormented her since the beginning of her marriage as she thought her dowry was not enough. Despite the fact that Julekha was pregnant, the beating and the scolding did not stop. Two weeks before her death, she had gone to her parents' house for a week. On her return, the abuse from her mother-in-law increased.

On the day of her death Julekha did all the housework but had nothing to eat. That evening she cried and talked to her husband about it, yet her mother-in-law still bullied her in front of her husband. That night, when Julekha's husband went to irrigate their rice paddy field, the mother-in-law and another neighbouring woman attacked Julekha. She resisted, but the women stuffed a blouse into her mouth so that no one heard her screams.

Her husband returned home from the field at about three in the morning. Julekha's mother-in-law told him that she had high blood pressure, was sleeping and should not be disturbed. Julekha's husband slept and went to work the following morning without realising that his wife was already dead. Later that morning, the mother-in-law put flour mixed with water in Julekha's hands, cut some potatoes beside her, and laid her on the ground. Then she went to the neighbour's house. After some time she went home and began to shout loudly that her daughter-in-law was dead. Neighbours and in-laws gathered around the body, her husband was sent for, and he informed Julekha's parents of her death.

Julekha's parents filed a murder case with the police and took her body to another city for an additional post-mortem examination. The original police report said Julekha had died from high blood pressure, but it was rumoured that Julekha's husband's family had bribed the police.

When Julekha was washed before her funeral, all of her jewelry was missing and a blouse hook was discovered in her mouth. Two sticks were also found in her birth canal – an assault to kill her baby. Julekha's parents believe that she and her unborn baby were killed brutally and robbed by her mother-in-law, who absconded.

From the White Ribbon Alliance for Safe Motherhood Bangladesh & MotherNewBorNet

Wasima Sultana

Wasima lived in Nagarpur in the Tangail District of Bangladesh. She was married at 18 and after 10 years became pregnant for the first time. When her labour pains started she was admitted to the Nagarpur Thana Health Complex. But her labour did not progress as expected. A Caesarean section was performed and a healthy baby boy was delivered.

After the surgery, Wasima experienced severe bleeding. She was given a blood transfusion and medication, and her condition stabilised for a few hours. But later that night she developed acute kidney failure; her heart rate increased and her blood pressure began to fall.

Wasima was immediately referred to the Tangail General Hospital, a district level secondary health care centre, for treatment. Her condition did not improve. She was referred to the Dhaka Medical College Hospital and arrived at the emergency department in a critical condition, suffering from shock and severe respiratory distress. The doctors did their best and placed her in an intensive care unit. But Wasima's heart stopped beating and doctors could not revive her. She was declared dead that night. The cause was heart and lung failure following the severe bleeding she experienced after her Caesarean section.

Wasima was 28 years old. She left behind a newborn who will never know his mother.

From the White Ribbon Alliance for Safe Motherhood Bangladesh & MotherNewBorNet

Bolivia

Delfina

Delfina lived with her husband and two children who were both born at home. She never learned to read or write. She had once been given contraceptive pills, but her husband was opposed and so she stopped taking them.

In 2005 Delfina was pregnant again, and in November she went to the health facility for her first visit. In February 2006, she went back for her third visit and everything seemed to be fine. But soon after, she started having headaches and was told her blood pressure had gone up.

On March 20th, at around 10 o'clock at night, Delfina had a severe headache and stomach pain. Her mother-in-law gave her herb tea and wet her head. Early the next morning, Delfina's sister-in-law went to the health facility to call the auxiliary nurse. But the nurse did not identify the danger signs and gave Delfina's sister-in-law a pain-reliever tablet to give to Delfina without examining her. An hour later, the auxiliary nurse went to Delfina's home to check on her. She measured her blood pressure and found it was very high. She consulted the doctor over the phone and was told to give Delfina a drug for high blood pressure. After some time, Delfina's blood pressure still had not dropped, so the nurse gave another tablet to Delfina and left.

After the second pill, Delfina's headache subsided, but at 10 o'clock she began vomiting and had convulsions. The nurse could not be found and Delfina's in-laws found a car to take her to the hospital where the doctor told her family she was in a critical condition. At 11:20pm the hospital diagnosed Delfina with convulsions related to high blood pressure. She went into a coma and died at 12:10pm. Her baby daughter was delivered by a post-mortem Caesarean section but died of breathing difficulties three days later. Delfina was 29 years old.

From the Safe Birth and Motherhood Committee, Bolivia

21

Burkina Faso

Fatou

Fatou was married to Amadou and they lived in the Patte d'Oie quarter of Ouagadougou. Fatou was very friendly and loved life dearly. She brought joy and happiness to her husband, family and many others in her community. She worked very hard every day from morning until evening.

Fatou loved children, but after three years of marriage the couple still had no children of their own and they began to worry. Fatou became sad, especially when she was alone – but in time, her sadness was transformed. She was pregnant and her joy was immense. She thanked God and sang songs as she worked. She imagined her child running about with the others, her face was lit by a divine, peaceful, and friendly smile.

Fatou began her visits to the health centre. When her child moved inside her, she was so delighted that she told everyone. When asked if she wanted a boy or a girl, she always said that, 'it doesn't matter, so long as it is born.'

One beautiful Friday morning after nine months she began to feel labour pains.

Her mother-in-law took Fatou to the health centre, and Amadou arrived as Fatou went into the delivery room; he could hear her suffering in her cries.

The delivery was difficult and Fatou lost a great deal of blood. She became so weak that she could no longer push. Her child had already died when the doctors decided that Fatou needed a Caesarean section to save her life. She was transferred by ambulance to another health centre where her husband waited. Time passed and the wait got longer and longer. When the doctor came out of the operating room he told Amadou that Fatou had died. Amadou blacked out and Fatou's mother-in-law was inconsolable. Her pain was enormous as she watched the bodies of Fatou and her baby girl taken to the morgue.

Fatou had wanted children so badly, but lost her own life in giving birth. She has left behind a family in sadness and a husband who still mourns to this day. Her death on November 29, 2005 was a great shock and brought much sadness to everyone who knew her. Fatou was 29 years old.

From the White Ribbon Alliance for Safe Motherhood Burkina Faso, Section Kadiogo

3 ANS DE MARIAGE

JOIE DE FATOU ET AMADOU

CONSULTATION PRENATALE

DÉCÈS DE FATOU

ENTERREMENT DE FATOU

IMPLICATION DE LA COMMUNAUTE DANS LA LI

Democratic Republic
of the Congo

Sisters Madeleine, Nzako & Bolumbu

In Beronge Village, in Bandundu Province, Democratic Republic of the Congo, Mother Anne had five daughters and two sons. Yet when they grew up, three of her five daughters died while giving birth.

Madeleine

Mother Anne's second daughter, Madeleine, married when she was 16 and soon became pregnant. While returning home from a trip to Kinshasa, Madeleine went into labour. She was in terrible pain and although she made it to a health post, she died before giving birth.

Nzako

Mother Anne's third daughter, Nzako, moved to Kinshasa to pursue her education. There she got married and became pregnant. Her husband was unemployed and so Nzako could not afford antenatal health care. When her baby was due, Nzako went to the closest health centre and spoke with the nurse at the door.

'Did you have [antenatal] visits here?' asked the nurse.

'No,' answered Nzako.

'How much money do you have?' asked the nurse.

'Two thousand Congolese francs (approximately £2).
I used the extra I had to come here,' said Nzako.

'Your case cannot be treated here,' continued the nurse. 'Go to Hôpital Général de Référence in Kinshasa.'

With her older sister, Nzako went to the hospital, but again she was asked how much money she had and was turned away. Nzako was told to go Bondeko Hospital, a further five kilometres away. Despite Nzako's pleas for help, she had to make her own way to Bondeko Hospital, but once she arrived at the door Nzako died.

Bolumbu

Mother Anne's fourth daughter, Bolumbu, stayed in their home village. She got married and had three children. Beronge is 150 kilometres away from the district hospital and can only be accessed by bicycle. Nearing the end of her fourth pregnancy she went to the health centre and was seen by a nurse. Yet when she went into labour there was no doctor, equipment or drugs to manage her complications. She died in front of her family and the nurses. Everyone was powerless and could do nothing to help her.

From the Maternité Sans Risque,
Democratic Republic of the Congo

Clockwise from top: Nzako, Bolumbu, Madeleine

Dominican Republic

Onesima Montero

Onesima died after giving birth at a hospital in the Dominican Republic in the early hours of October 20, 2005. She was found by her relatives when they came to visit her between two and six o'clock in the afternoon. She died from heavy bleeding. The doctors and nurses had never checked on Onesima in the hours after she gave birth. She had been completely wrapped up because of the cold that women can experience after giving birth, and for this reason no one realised her state, nor did they investigate. Onesima was 29 years old.

This story was collected by a team working to discover why so many women die in the Dominican Republic – despite comparatively good education and access to health care. This suggests that the quality of maternity care in the Dominican Republic is poor.

Onesima clearly died of neglect. Many women's lives could be saved if health care workers were better trained, and held accountable for their treatment of women.

From the University of California, Berkeley, School of Public Health – Maternal & Child Health Department, USA

Ethiopia

Yeruknesh Mesfin

Yeruknesh was born in a village called Goradit, which means 'cut-off.' Her parents were poor farmers and she never had the chance to go to school; from the age of seven Yeruknesh looked after her family's cattle.

Ten days after her birth Yeruknesh was circumcised by an old woman from her village. Then, at aged 13, while gathering fire wood, she was abducted, raped by and married to a local farmer, Mr. Zena. He was 32 years old and his first wife had died. Yeruknesh became stepmother to his four-year-old son and two-year-old daughter.

Yeruknesh got up very early to prepare breakfast for the family. It was a half a kilometre walk to fetch water in a pot. She took care of the children and the livestock, gathered wood and sometimes helped her husband weed and collect the harvest. Every evening she cooked, got the house in order, and was always the last to go to bed. She never had time to rest. If she went out to visit neighbours without her husband's knowledge he beat her, accusing her of laziness. He gave no value to the work she performed for him and his children.

Shortly after her marriage, Yeruknesh started menstruating and became pregnant. She dreamed that her firstborn would be a boy.

Yeruknesh felt serious pain and discomfort during her pregnancy, but carried on with her daily work. She faced the birth alone with no one to advise her.

As the time for the birth approached, Yeruknesh put on locally made ragged cloths and lay on a piece of matting on her hut's floor. Tightly clutching her pillow she called repeatedly for her mother, while tears flowed down her cheeks. The whole of her body trembled and she became terrified. She was in agony and her body was wracked by sweat and intense fever.

A few women neighbours came into Yeruknesh's small thatched grass hut. Their faces constricted in sympathy. One of them lit a candle and they prayed to God that Yeruknesh would deliver safely. Mr. Zena called for the traditional birth attendant of the village to help Yeruknesh, who was now in critical condition. The complications were far beyond the capacity of the traditional birth attendant, who had no formal training, so Mr. Zena asked the men of the village to carry Yeruknesh to Bahir Dar Hospital.

Yeruknesh made it to the hospital, but both she and her baby died. The next day her body was taken back to the village and buried in the graveyard of St. Mary's church. Yeruknesh was 15 years old.

From the Medico Socio Development Assistance of Ethiopia

India

Kuntakala Parteke

Kuntakala Parteke was the third daughter of Mahadev Parteke, a poor labourer, and his wife, Sharada, from the village of Kampthi-Khanapur. Known to her family as 'Kunti', she studied for only two years at the government school before leaving to help her family at home and in the fields. A playful child, Kunti was popular with her friends and neighbours.

When she reached the age of 20, Kunti was married to Pralhad Maraskolhe in a 'Samuhik Vivaha Sohala' (community marriage ceremony) on the recommendation of a relative. Brought up in a traditional culture, Kunti did not complain, even when her husband began to drink heavily and abuse her.

A year later, Kunti became pregnant. Despite her initial joy, the hardships continued at home. Kunti's antenatal care was neglected and her health began to suffer. One afternoon she was taken to the rural hospital in a state of shock, her legs and hands swollen. She was immediately referred to the district hospital, but her husband refused to take her, instead leaving Kunti with her parents.

As Kunti's condition deteriorated, Mahadev and Sharada rushed their daughter to Sewagram Hospital, where doctors performed an emergency operation. Tragically, it was too late to save Kunti or her child.

From the Dr. Sushila Nayar School of Public Health, Mahatma Gandhi Institute of Medical Sciences, India

Sunita Shankar Narnavare

Sunita Shankar Narnavare was born on May 2, 1981 in Wadaki, a tribal village in the Yavatmal District of Maharashtra, India. The youngest of four children, her parents were farmers and she studied at the village government school. Married at aged 19 to a resident of Anji Village in the Wardha District, Sunita got along well with her new family and neighbours, and they were fond of her. Every day after finishing her household chores, she would help her husband with farm work.

During her second pregnancy Sunita attended the Bal Suraksha Diwas maternal and child health centre day in the village; she also received regular checkups and antenatal care. Following tradition, family members made the decision to send her to her own parent's village for the baby's birth. So after eight months of pregnancy she went to her maternal home to prepare.

On January 5, 2007, Sunita developed labour pains and was seen by the local registered medical practitioner in a nearby village. The doctor tried his best to deliver the baby, but as Sunita's pains grew worse he decided to refer her to the district hospital.

It was now late at night and Sunita was helpless. The hospital was 75 kilometres away and it was extremely difficult to get transportation. With the help of the community members, she eventually reached the hospital early the following morning. Even in her semi-conscious state she was able to deliver her baby boy normally, but the birth left Sunita exhausted and bleeding profusely. She had experienced postpartum haemorrhage and it took the hospital time to arrange blood for a transfusion. Even though the doctors tried their best and Sunita received four units of blood, she could not be saved. Sunita bid farewell to the world on January 6, 2007; her newborn son died the same day.

Sunita Shankar Narnavare's death has been mourned by her community. Her fabric panel was displayed at the Safe Motherhood and Child Survival Campaign that took place in her village and in another neighbouring village. Community members organised the first Safe Motherhood Days to raise awareness in nearby villages and developed an Emergency Transport Plan in Sunita's memory. All in the hope that no more women will die needlessly in pregnancy or childbirth.

From the Dr. Sushila Nayar School of Public Health, Mahatma Gandhi Institute of Medical Sciences, India

Vaishali Subhash Devtale

Vaishali Subhash Devtale, the fourth daughter of a poor farmer in Pawnar, was brought up in a very traditional way. After twelve years of education, she was married at the age of 22 to Subhash, a welder with a workshop in Wardha.

Vaishali was very jovial and intelligent; she just knew how to keep everyone happy. Helpful, hard-working and understanding, her in-laws who didn't have a daughter came to love her in a very short amount of time.

The news of Vaishali's pregnancy was celebrated by both families, and she received very special care. After six months, Vaishali's parents insisted she return to their rural home to give birth, as is the custom.

But Vaishali's labour was complicated and soon she needed an emergency Caesarean operation and an urgent blood transfusion. She was rushed to a nearby city, Chandrapur, and two bags of blood were sent for, but they arrived 20 minutes too late.

Miraculously, her baby son survived, and is now two years old and living with Vaishali's parents. Subhash misses him.

'Time has been very harsh on me,' he says. 'I cannot forget Vaishali. It has been very difficult, but life must go on. My parents persuaded me to get married again, but Vaishali lives here too. I keep her photograph on the wall.'

From the Dr. Sushila Nayar School of Public Health, Mahatma Gandhi Institute of Medical Sciences, India

Subhadra Sa
From DREAM India, The Society for
Development of Rural Economy and Manpower

Sita Bhoi
From DREAM India, The Society for
Development of Rural Economy and Manpower

Surekha Kumbhar

Surekha Kumbhar was 21 years old and married when she became pregnant for the first time. Regarded by all as a valued member of the community, she had already served for three years as the President of the Budima Self Help Group. She taught other women how to read and write, and worked in her village to mobilize others to keep the village roads clean.

Surekha delivered a baby girl on June 19, 2007 at the district hospital in Balangir. But after returning home from the hospital, she experienced complications. She died just a few days later, leaving the newborn baby alone with her husband.

From DREAM India, The Society for Development of Rural Economy and Manpower

Murrabai Majhi

From the Society for Rural Upliftment
& Socio Technological Initiative of India

Munge Hans

*From the Society for Rural Upliftment
& Socio Technological Initiative of India*

Saibani Kata

*From the Society for Rural Upliftment
& Socio Technological Initiative of India*

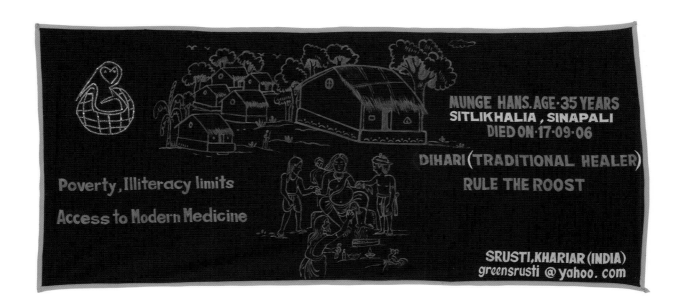

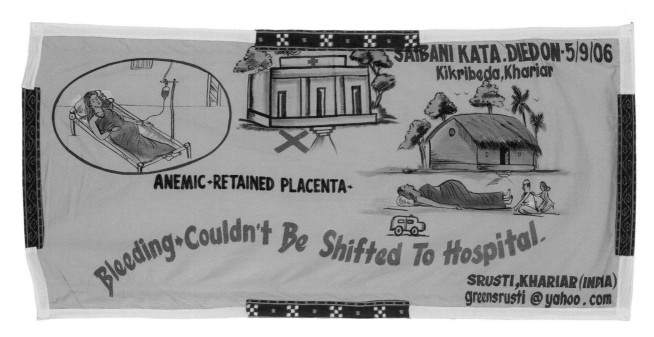

Jayanti Meher

From the Society for Rural Upliftment
& Socio Technological Initiative of India

Upasi Sabar

From the Society for Rural Upliftment
& Socio Technological Initiative of India

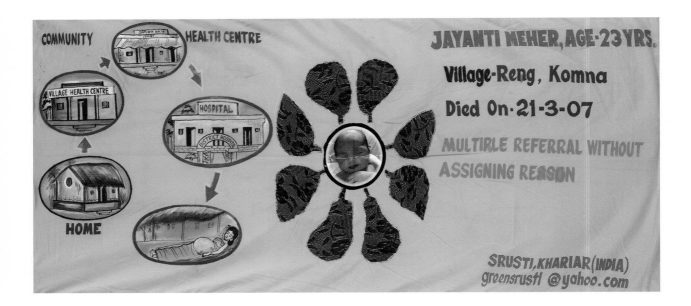

Balmati Rout

From the Society for Rural Upliftment
& Socio Technological Initiative of India

Remati Bag

From the Society for Rural Upliftment
& Socio Technological Initiative of India

Sapna

Sapna belonged to a community of snake charmers who had moved from Rajasthan to Delhi to make their living.

Sapna was a fun loving person with great respect for her elders; her dream was to provide education for her children. Although she always received good antenatal care, Sapna was afraid of what would happen if she went to the hospital.

Two of her babies were born safely at home, but the third birth was dangerously complicated. Sapna needed emergency hospital care to save her life, but she was too scared to take that step; she died soon after giving birth.

From the Community Aid & Sponsorship Programme of India

GRANDMA

AUNT

FRI CHW

TBA

FRIEND

DECEASED HOME

CALCIUM

DOCTOR

Indonesia

R.A. Kartini

From the Indonesian Midwives Association

Fighter for the advancement for young girls & women in Indonesia through opportunity for equal education.

It was a great lost when her efforts to fight for the advancement of all young girls & women in the country was cut short, because of her death in child birth.

Siti Nurjanah Binti Erna

Siti died eight years ago after giving birth to her sixth child. Like most women from her village, she worked very hard even while pregnant. She awoke before the sun rose each morning and did her household duties until late in the evening. Although she cooked all the meals, she did not eat with her family. Instead, she ate after everyone else had eaten, which often meant that she did not get enough food. While expecting her last child she developed iron deficiency anaemia and did not receive any antenatal care. Because she had gone through childbirth without complications five times before, her sixth pregnancy was not viewed any differently.

Though there was a trained midwife in a village nearby, Siti's family decided to ask the traditional birth attendant in their village to assist with the birth. But when Siti went into labour, complications arose, and she suffered from severe bleeding.

As the decision makers of the family were away from home at the time, Siti was not brought to a health care facility until two hours had elapsed. By then it was too late to save her life. Siti died because of delays in seeking and receiving care, like so many women in Indonesia.

From the White Ribbon Alliance for Safe Motherhood Indonesia, Aliansi Pita Putih Indonesia

Kenya

Wambui

Wambui was a 32 year-old single mother who made her living selling items at a street market in Nairobi. When she was twenty-eight weeks pregnant, Wambui was admitted to hospital with ruptured membranes and a fever. But even after a full week of treatment, her condition had not improved. Her doctors decided to perform a hysterectomy. When they began to operate, they discovered a catheter inside Wambui's abdomen.

Wambui later admitted that she had visited an unqualified street abortionist. She had been reluctant to tell her story when she was first admitted because the nurses she spoke to were openly hostile to her. Abortion, though commonplace, remains taboo throughout much of Kenya; the law prohibits abortion unless it can be proved that a woman's life is in danger.

After the surgery, Wambui's health continued to deteriorate. She died ten days later.

Sadly, her story is not uncommon. Every year, tens of thousands of women die from complications relating to unsafe abortion; even more are seriously injured.

From Ipas, USA

Malawi

Zione Mchepa

Zione Mcheba was from the Chipaka village of Dowa in Malawi. She died in July 1998, when she was just 14 years old.

Zione was pregnant for the first time and was told by her family she must deliver her baby at home, even though she had been advised to deliver with a skilled attendant in a hospital. When Zione's labour started, she experienced complications. The baby was too big and Zione needed a Caesarean section.

While waiting for a decision to be made by her family to arrange transport and take her to the hospital, Zione lost her life.

From the White Ribbon Alliance
for Safe Motherhood, Malawi

Dedicated to 14 year old Zione Mchepa. Cultural practices deterred her from accessing skilled care

Gertrude Chisi

From the White Ribbon Alliance for Safe Motherhood, Malawi

Julita Lotia

From the White Ribbon Alliance for Safe Motherhood, Malawi

Leya Chigwadire

From the White Ribbon Alliance for Safe Motherhood, Malawi

IN MEMORY OF GETRUDE CHISI
If transport was readily availble, she could have been alive
DIED IN JULY 2004

JULITA   LOTIA
Died in 1997 at 22 years. She had problems accessing skilled care.

LEYA CHIGWADIRE
A victim of lack of awareness by relatives cost her life.
SHE DIED IN 1989

Nepal

Tulasha Shrestha

This panel is dedicated to the memory of Tulasha by her three daughters, Pushpa, Tumsa and Binjwala, and her granddaughter, Akriti. Tulasha is symbolised as a strong tree, growing and evolving through the many stages of motherhood. The baby at the base of the tree reaches out to its mother, in search of food, love, and comfort, while the roots have drops of blood at the tips to symbolise the bleeding Tulasha endured each time after giving birth. Her braided hair is mirrored by the bent branches of the tree. As the branches hang lower we see a woman who feels helpless and is slowly losing her life while giving birth to her fifth child. The heart-shaped leaves represent the love and affection of Tulasha's four surviving children and grandchildren, while other leaves depict the many talents of the mother they have lost.

The backdrop of the panel includes scenes of the Nepalese village Tulasha lived in a mountainous rural area far from roads and services.

*From The Safe Motherhood
Network Federation, Nepal*

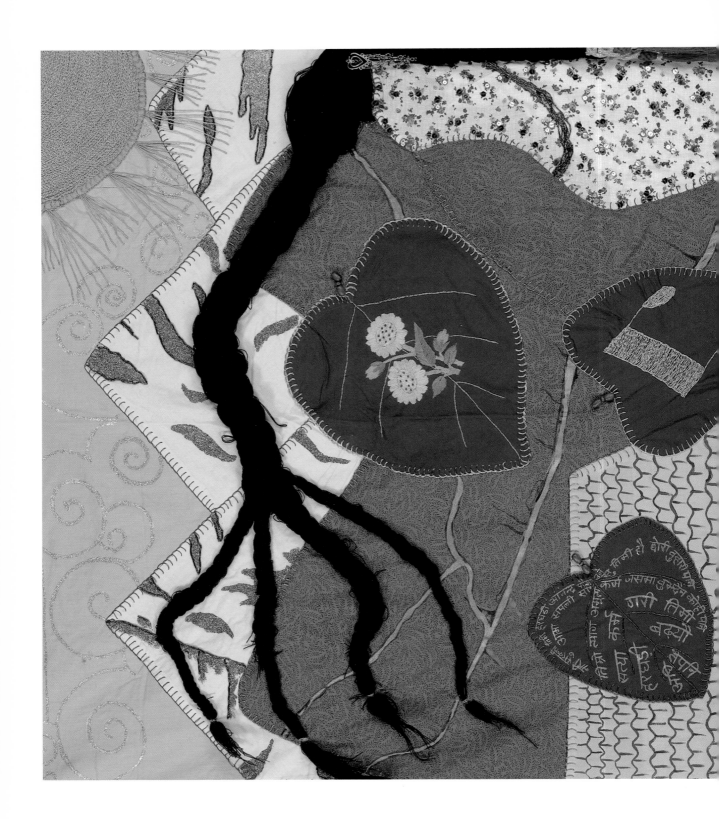

Nigeria

Ukamaka Adonu

Ukamaka was 21 years old and six months pregnant when she died. Married shortly after she completed secondary school, she lived with her husband Chukwuemeka in Enugu. One morning Ukamaka complained of dizziness, of feeling cold and of an irregular heartbeat. Her husband did not think her symptoms were serious and left for work, only to receive a phone call later to say that his wife had been admitted to the hospital.

At the local hospital, the doctor did not find anything wrong with Ukamaka. Prescribing bed rest and a saline drip, he planned to discharge her the next day. Chukwuemeka left Ukamaka with her sister while he went to get money to pay the hospital bill and some food. While he was gone, Ukamaka talked and joked with her sister before taking a nap.

But when the sister tried to wake Ukamaka later, she could not. The doctor came into the room to find that Ukamaka had died. She was buried on Saturday, June 9, 2007. She left behind her husband, her parents, her siblings, and a family that loved her very much.

From the Women Information Network of Nigeria

ACCESS TO HIGH QUALITY HEALTHCARE SERVICES COULD HAVE SAVED THE LIFE OF THIS PREGNANT WOMAN!

UKAMAKA ADONU
APRIL 3, 1986 - MAY 28, 2007

Enugu State Nigeria.

Chidimma Obinna

Chidimma was from a rich and prominent family, while her boyfriend Chidi came from a very poor family. When Chidimma got pregnant, she was disowned by her parents who sent her to Chidi's house. Three times, Chidi's mother Jean tried to send her back, but the family would not accept her.

Jean, a widow, reluctantly gave the couple a small room but never fed or took care of the pregnant girl. Chidi had no job and could not take care of her either.

Chidimma had to live by scavenging, wandering over 10 kilometres into the bush everyday in search of palm kernel, which she cracked and sold in the market for a meagre amount. With this she could only make soup and garri to live on for a week. She became a part of the night, as her songs and cracking of kernels were heard through the darkness.

Chidimma had no health care until her labour pains started on the morning of June 13, 2002. Alone she crawled half a kilometre to the main road. She went to an unregistered clinic which had been closed down by the government, where she laboured on a mat for two days, battling against mosquitoes in the cold. Here Chidimma spent her last days without water or food. On June 15th, she gave birth to twins who, like their mother, died.

The deaths reconciled the two families who cried as the remains of poor Chidimma were lowered into mother earth, and heaps of sand were poured on her wooden coffin. It was the only time she received affection from them.

From the Friends in Life Education Peer Club of Nigeria

Monica Odunzegbulem

From the Love in Action Community Initiative of Nigeria

Edo Uduak

From the Live for Tomorrow Movement of Nigeria

Boma Ben

From the Live for Tomorrow Movement of Nigeria

DELAY IN MAKING DECISION.
AVAILABILITY OF EMERGENCY MEDICAL CAR/FACILITY, DOCTOR

BABY

Rita Egwe

Rita was 25 years old and lived in the inaccessible riverside community of Afono Erei in Cross River State. When she went into labour, she was helped by one of the community's traditional birth attendants. But complications began and the birth attendant referred her to another traditional birth attendant living seven kilometres away.

Reaching there after a difficult journey across rough roads by motorcycle, Rita found there was no one available to help. She was put in a bed where she waited for the birth attendant to return. Rita died during labour on July 19, 2007.

From the Centre for Healthworks,
Development and Research of Nigeria

Rose Anietie

From the Centre for Healthworks,
Development and Research of Nigeria

ROSE
ANIETIE

BORN:
1979
DIED:
AUGUST
7, 2007

ALL DREAMS STOPPED FOR ROSE, AS HER
HUSBAND BEAT HER, EVEN WITH PREGNANCY
TILL THE VERY END.

Pakistan

Zakia Bibi

This is the story of Zakia, who was married to Muhammad Akhtar and died during labour. Zakia and Muhammad lived in a remote village of the Khanewal District in Pakistan. There are no doctors or health workers in the basic health unit in the village. The Pakistan Lions Youth Council organisation started working there as a part of the Pakistan Initiative for Mothers and Newborns. While visiting families to provide information about antenatal and postnatal care, community health workers (CHW) met Zakia who was in her ninth month of pregnancy. Zakia was feeling pain in her lower abdomen. The CHW advised Muhammad to take Zakia to see a doctor for a check-up and to make arrangements to ensure a safe delivery when Zakia went into labour.

Meanwhile, a traditional birth attendant (TBA) told Zakia's family members that the baby was not positioned well, thus she advised them to take Zakia to the hospital. The head of the family ignored the TBA and Zakia's pain became severe. Ten days later, another CHW visited the house and was able to motivate Zakia's family members to take her to the hospital. Even though the family had money to arrange transportation to the hospital by an ambulance or taxi, they took their ox cart to save money. The village was 25 kilometres away from the hospital and it was a long trip in the slow ox cart. Halfway to the hospital, Zakia began bleeding severely and died.

The delay in making the decision to bring Zakia to the hospital and the delay in transporting her to care led to her unfortunate death. Zakia's husband Muhammad now advises people in his village about these issues.

From the Pakistan Lions Youth Council

Kundan Mai

Kundan was assisted by a traditional birth attendant, a Dai, during her delivery. She experienced complications during her labour and was advised to seek help at the nearest health care facility. An ambulance was not available to take Kundan, so another vehicle had to be arranged to transport her to a hospital. Kundan arrived at the rural health centre at Kot-Chutta where a staff shortage prevented her from receiving care. Kundan died at the health centre.

From Youth Front Pakistan

Detail
Khatiza Mai

Khatiza had no health care during her pregnancy. She lacked information about health, and there were no medical facilities available to her locally. There were no vehicles to take her to the hospital, and the government failed to provide her with one. Khatiza, trapped by tribal traditions and no education, died of heavy bleeding during the delivery.

From Youth Front Pakistan

Najma

Sakina, Najma's younger sister, told this story:

'There was no education for the girls in our family. Najma was married at 21 to Shahmir, a mechanic. On her wedding day she looked like a princess. After one year she gave birth to a daughter. Her in-laws were disappointed as they wanted a boy. But Najma loved her daughter Sadia very much. She was like a butterfly and Najma made shiny, bright coloured clothes for her.

Two years later Najma had another baby girl, Gulmena, and her disappointed husband and in-laws ignored her and the new baby.

In her third pregnancy, Najma prayed to God for help. But her third baby was also a girl and her husband threatened to divorce her, while her mother-in-law taunted her that she would arrange a second marriage for her son.

Najma became very weak and pale, working hard with little food to eat. Our mother took her to the hospital and they found she was anaemic with high blood pressure and pregnant again. But her husband and in-laws wanted a male child so badly that she continued with the pregnancy. In her eighth month Najma started to bleed heavily and her in-laws were forced to take her to the hospital. The doctor advised immediate surgery, but it was too late and she died.

Najma's three daughters have suffered. Sadia is now six and looks after her siblings. When someone asks about her mother, her eyes well up with tears. I tell the girls – our three little Najmas – that their mother is a star in the sky. They wonder why so many mothers have had to leave their children.'

From Blue Veins – Women Welfare & Relief Services of Pakistan

*From Blue Veins – Women Welfare
& Relief Services of Pakistan*

Husan Pari

Saeeda Bibi, from Mardan in the North West Frontier province, tells of her daughter who died in childbirth at the age of 13:

'She was the only child God gave to me, an angel so lovely that we called her Husan Pari, meaning pretty fairy. But her luck was not pretty and when she was eight, her father died in a road accident. I worried that if I died too, who would take care of my daughter?
I wanted her to get married, to be happy and secure. I found a match for her; a farmer in a nearby village. Husan Pari was very excited about her wedding and her new clothes, but she did not know what marriage would bring.

Within three months she was pregnant and I took her to the traditional birth attendant, the Dai, who gave her remedies for vomiting. We could pay the Dai in small installments and we liked her prayers and herbs. Our grandmothers say that birth can bring death and the forces that keep a woman alive are strongest in the home.

Husan Pari worked very hard and her diet was poor – superstitions stopped her from eating eggs and fish. She became terribly thin. I worried how she would bear the pain of labour; I didn't know that my daughter, the heart and light of my eyes, would die.

The worst time came on June 26, 2005. We went to help her when we heard her screams but the baby would not emerge. The Dai became nervous, refused to help anymore and said we must take her to the hospital. On the way, Husan Pari became blue, cold as ice and died in my arms. I could not save her or her baby. I cannot remember how we reached home, or how the funeral happened. The pain was unbearable.

Husan Pari could have lived if she had skilled health care and not married so young. I blame myself for her death.'

*From Blue Veins – Women Welfare
& Relief Services of Pakistan*

OUT OF THE 30,000 WOMEN WHO LOSE THEIR LIVES YEARLY IN PAKISTAN DUE TO POOR MATERNAL HEALTH CARE, THE MAJORITY ARE FIRST TIME MOTHERS.

WE HONOR THE MEMORY OF THE WOMEN WHOSE LIVES FADED AWAY BEFORE THE *HENNA* ON THEIR HANDS DID.

From the White Ribbon Alliance
for Safe Motherhood, Pakistan

Nazeer Bibi

Throughout her pregnancy, Nazeer worked in the fields with her husband. One day she felt pain and told her husband. He found an ox cart to take her to the nearest village for help, but on the way her pain and bleeding were so great that they stopped while local women gathered to help her. They held up cloths to protect her privacy but had no midwifery training. One woman pressed down on Nazeer's belly with her foot which made her cry out and bleed all the more. Other locals arrived and told her husband that he must send for a trained midwife or Nazeer would die. He refused and told a male worker not to go near his wife.

An hour later Nazeer and her baby died under the open sky. All had witnessed this woman lose her life needlessly.

From the Yar Muhammad Samejo Educational Society & Development Organization of Pakistan

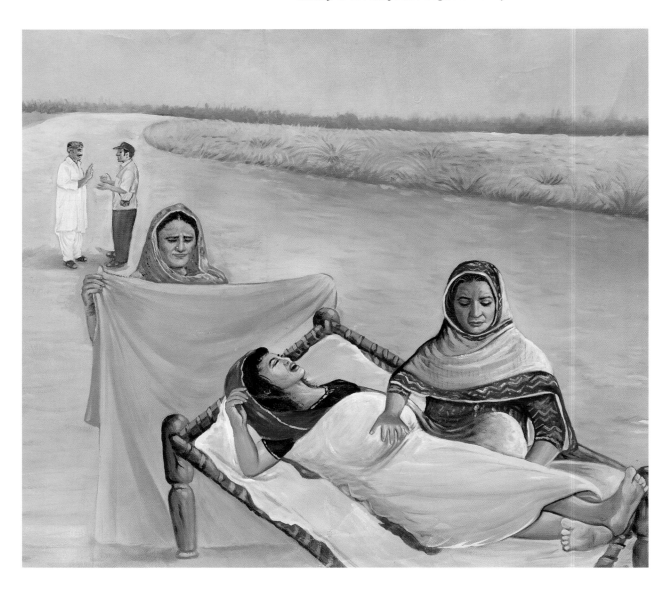

Hajra Hakeem

Hajra was married to Muhammad Hakeem. They lived in the Union Council Qubola Village of Mawa Khan Tehsil of Usta Muhammad. When she became pregnant, Hajra attended maternal and newborn health educational sessions. However, she did not visit a clinic or traditional birth attendant during her pregnancy for a checkup or antenatal care.

As is custom in Hajra's community, there is a stigma attached to visiting clinics, even when husbands are present and the health worker is female. So, although Hajra felt pain during her pregnancy she was not allowed to seek care, and was beaten and emotionally abused when she asked to be able to leave home and receive care.

Hajra completed her pregnancy without health care and a proper diet. When she went into labour she was left alone in a room to give birth without help, which is the custom. Hajra was crying in pain and demanded help, but no one came to her aid. She delivered a baby boy and died shortly thereafter. The baby also died.

From the Yar Muhammad Samejo Educational Society & Development Organization of Pakistan

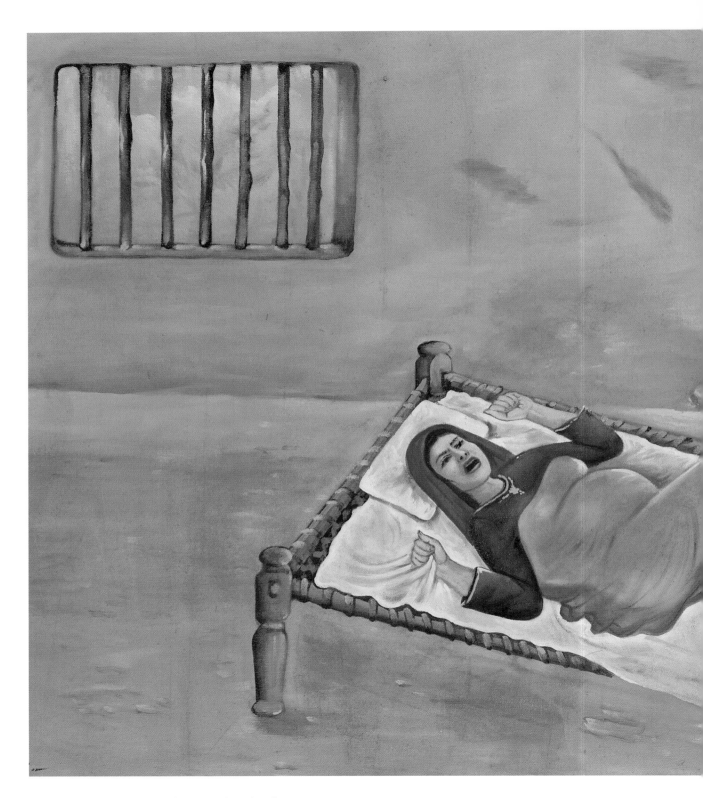

From the Yar Muhammad Samejo Educational
Society & Development Organization of Pakistan

Panama

Gertrudis Sire

This panel is dedicated to Gertrudis and all the indigenous Ngobe women of Panama that suffer every day because they have no access to their reproductive rights. The text on the panel reads:

'Dedicated to all the women of Panama who have suffered and died before, during and after childbirth.'

From the Asociacion de Mujeres Ngobes, Panama

Tanzania

Restituta Mwagu

Restituta was born in 1972 and passed away on March 7, 2006. Eleven years of her life were spent happily married to Paul Bonaventure Mligo, living in Likuyu Fussi Village of the Songea District Council in the Ruvuma Region of Tanzania. She was a very dedicated woman and cared deeply for her family. She worked on their farm and took care of other domestic activities so that she could earn a daily living and sustain her family. She was a well-known, hard-working, and loved woman in her village. Restituta had complications with her labour while she was at the nearby health care centre. It was decided that she needed to be referred to Peramiho Mission Hospital for a Caesarean section operation. It was difficult to find available transportation or an ambulance to the hospital. Restituta made the 47 kilometre ride to the hospital on a bicycle. Due to delay in finding transportation, and the slow and uncomfortable ride on the bicycle to the hospital, Restituta lost her life shortly after the Caesarean section operation. She left her husband, eight children and newborn daughter Rose behind.

From the Orphans Relief Services of Tanzania

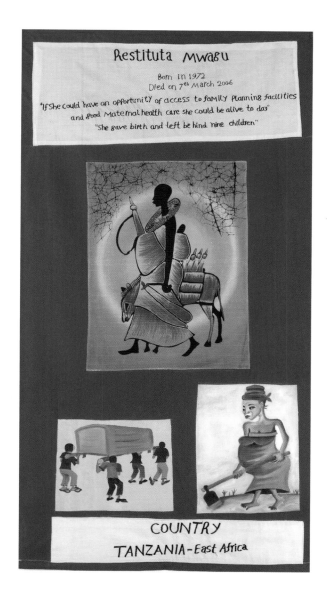

Sijawa Yasin

Sijawa was born in 1982 in the Mpingi Village of the Songea District Council in the Ruvuma Region of Tanzania. She was the fifth child of a family with eleven children. Sijawa passed away in May of 2004. Her older sister Khadija also died in childbirth in August of 1999.

Sijawa was not able to finish her primary school education because she was pregnant while in school at the age of 14. She delivered her first child through a Caesarean section operation and became pregnant again one year later.

When nine months pregnant with her second child, Sijawa was supposed to be referred to the Ruvuma Regional Hospital to have her child through another Caesarean section. When Sijawa started having labour pains, her family looked for transportation to take her to the hospital. However, they could not find any means of transportation quickly and the hospital was 78 kilometres from their village. In addition, many of the roads were impassable since it was the rainy season.

Sijawa's parents finally were able to arrange for the village tractor to take her to the hospital. The tractor was being used to go buy fertilizer in the town centre, and the family was lucky to secure a ride. The journey was a very painful experience for Sijawa; the ride was slow and tiresome. It became very hard and unbearable for Sijawa to persist in her condition, and she lost all her strength. She passed away while on the tractor.

From Orphans Relief Services of Tanzania

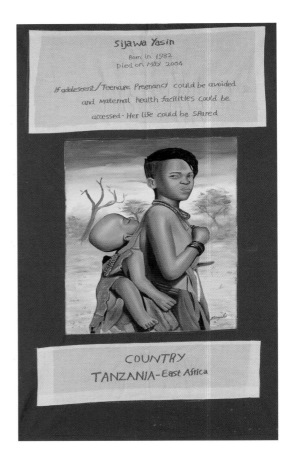

Uganda

Agnes Tusabe Nalongo

Agnes, a mother of twins, was honoured in her culture. She was the Secretary for Women on the local Council. She came from a poor family, so when she went into labour during her second pregnancy she was taken to the unskilled traditional birth attendant. Two days later and close to death, Agnes was taken to the hospital for a Caesarean section.

But Agnes' uterus had ruptured and her baby boy was already dead. After four days, Agnes was sent home. Yet she had lost too much blood during her operation and subsequently died of anaemia. Agnes' death was a disaster for her husband, family and the whole community.

From the Uganda Private Midwives Association

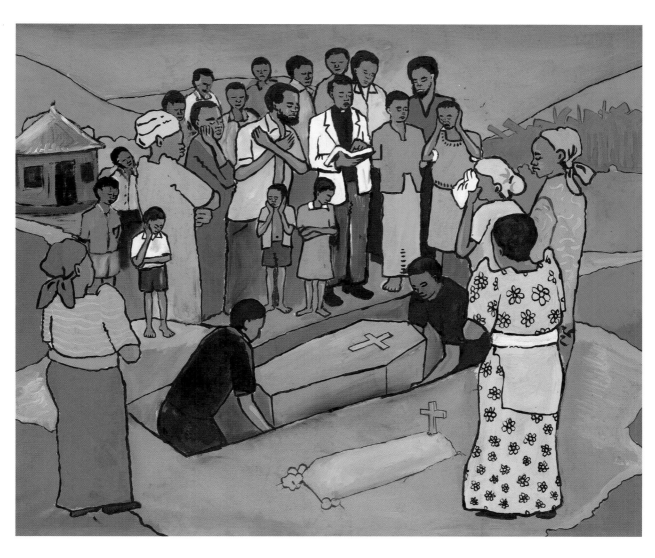

Linda Alina

From the Uganda Private Midwives Association

Dr. Cecilia Achadu Otim

At 34, Cecilia was the youngest and only female heart surgeon in Uganda. She was exceptionally talented and kind. She was dedicated to her patients and popular with the children of her community who enjoyed Sunday school in her home. After a healthy pregnancy, her daughter was born by Caesarean section in Mulago Hospital, Uganda's national referral hospital. But an hour after the operation, Cecilia's breathing changed and her mother insisted on calling a nurse. No nurse came and only her mother was there to hold Cecilia's hand as she breathed her last. Thousands attended her funeral, mourning the loss of a talented and much loved young woman, who was also a great asset and investment for the future of the country.

From the Naguru Teenage Information
& Health Centre of Straight Talk, Uganda

Sister Zuwagga

From the Women in Development Association
of Njeru & Maama Omwaana of Uganda

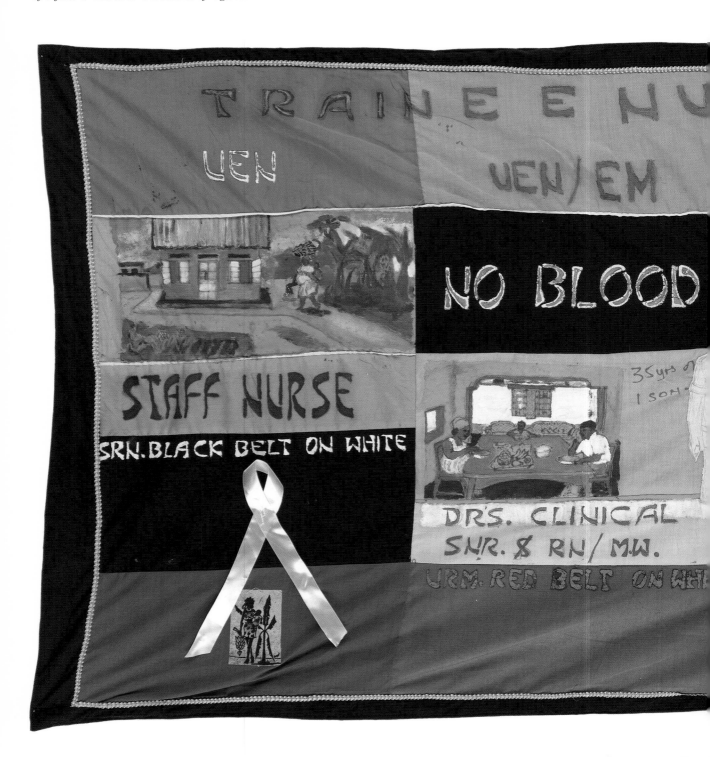

Amina Nambi

Amina was a 15 year old student when she became pregnant. She refused to reveal the father's name and ran away from home to the house of her baby's father. He told her to hide indoors in case she was imprisoned for defilement. So Amina never received antenatal care or any medical advice.

When she went into labour, there were complications and she was taken to the hospital. The doctor planned a Caesarean section, but Amina was anaemic and because of delays in procuring blood supplies, she and her baby both died.

The baby's father wrote a note and sent it to Amina's home, after which he disappeared, leaving the dead bodies in the hospital. The girl's relatives collected the bodies and buried them.

From the Women in Development Association of Njeru & Maama Omwaana of Uganda

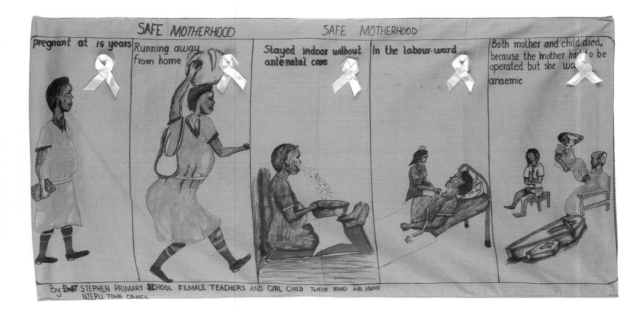

Agness Hamulesi

When Agness got pregnant, she was dismissed from school and her parents sent her away. She did odd jobs like cleaning to survive, but sometimes she had to beg for food and money. A midwife advised her to have the baby in a hospital, but because Agness was so malnourished and anaemic she died shortly after the birth. Her death was announced on the radio by the hospital authorities. Her mother was very hurt and regretted having abandoned her daughter. She collected the baby and Agness' body from the hospital, but the child died of malaria six months later.

From the Women in Development Association of Njeru & Maama Omwaana of Uganda

Mukiga

From the Women in Development Association
of Njeru & Maama Omwaana of Uganda

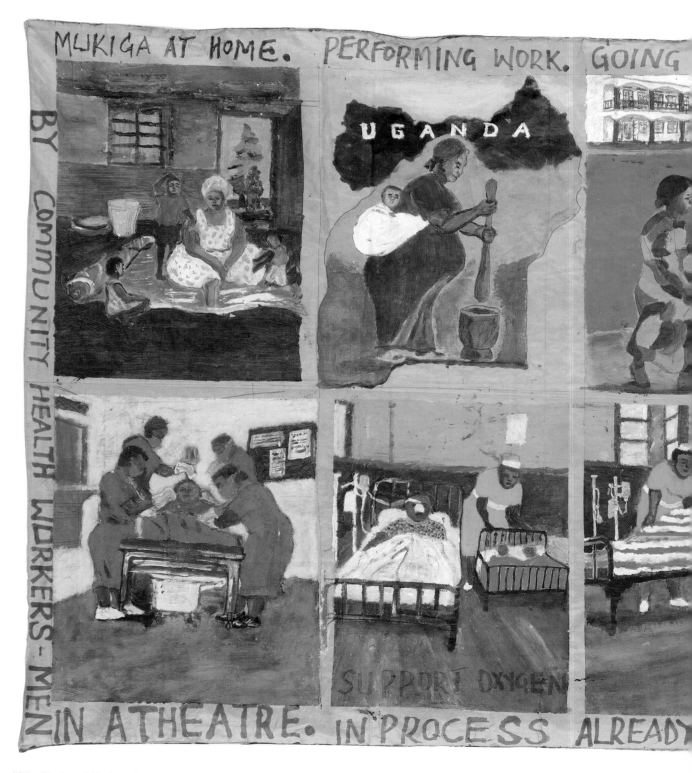

Participating Organisations

Afghan Midwives Association, Afghanistan

Asociacion de Mujeres Ngobes, Panama

Association of Gynaecologists and
Obstetricians, Tanzania

Blue Veins – Women Welfare & Relief
Services, Pakistan

CARE, Tanzania

Centre for Healthworks, Development
and Research, Nigeria

Community Aid and Sponsorship
Programme, India

Development Alternatives Through
Research & Innovative Action, India

Dr. Sushila Nayar School of Public Health,
Mahatma Gandhi Institute of Medical
Sciences, India

DREAM India, The Society for Development
of Rural Economy and Manpower

Friends in Life Education Peer Club, Nigeria

Grass Root Development
Programmes, Liberia

Health and Technical Education
Development Centre, Nepal

Indonesian Midwives Association, Indonesia

Ipas, United States of America

Jeevan Rekha Parishad, India

JHPIEGO, Tanzania

Lions Youth Council, Pakistan

Live for Tomorrow Movement, Nigeria

Love in Action Community Initiative, Nigeria

Maternité Sans Risque,
Democratic Republic of the Congo

Mbale Care & Support Trust, Uganda

Medico Socio Development
Assistance, Ethiopia

Naguru Teenage Information & Health
Centre of Straight Talk, Uganda

Organization For Good Life of the
Marginalized, Uganda

Orphans Relief Services, Tanzania

Safe Birth and Motherhood
Committee, Bolivia

Safe Motherhood Network Federation, Nepal

Society for Rural Upliftment & Socio
Technological Initiative, India

St. John's Hospital, Tanzania

TAMA, Tanzanian Midwifery Association

The Safe Motherhood Quilt Project,
United States of America

Uganda Private Midwives Association

University of California, Berkeley, School of
Public Health – Maternal & Child Health
Department, United States of America

White Ribbon Alliance for Safe Motherhood
Bangladesh & MotherNewBorNet

White Ribbon Alliance for Safe Motherhood
Burkina Faso, Section Kadiogo

White Ribbon Alliance
for Safe Motherhood, India

White Ribbon Alliance for Safe Motherhood
Indonesia, Aliansi Pita Putih Indonesia

White Ribbon Alliance
for Safe Motherhood, Malawi

White Ribbon Alliance
for Safe Motherhood, Pakistan

White Ribbon Alliance
for Safe Motherhood, Tanzania

Women in Development Association of Njeru
& Maama Omwaana, Uganda

Women Information Network, Nigeria

Women's Dignity Project, Tanzania

Yar Muhammad Samejo Educational Society
& Development Organization, Pakistan

Youth Front Pakistan

Participating Organisations at work around the world

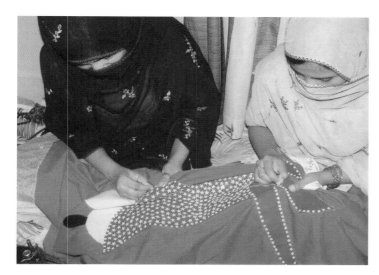

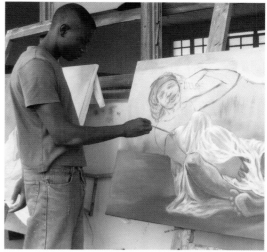

The Promise to
Mothers Lost Campaign

Every minute, somewhere in the world, a woman dies in pregnancy or childbirth

Almost all who die are in the developing world and without access to health services. Half of the world's women still give birth alone, or with only a neighbour or relative to help. In the poorest regions, women face at least a one in eight chance of dying from pregnancy related causes.

We know that these deaths can be prevented. So why do the grim statistics stay the same, decade after decade?

Now is the time for change

Pressure for change is building, especially from the communities and countries that have lost so many of their daughters, sisters, wives, and friends. Making heard these voices and listening to these experiences are a major step towards righting one of the world's great injustices.

White Ribbon Alliance members spanning 91 countries are calling for politicians and public officials everywhere to ensure every woman's right – to life saving midwifery and obstetric care. Everywhere in the world, women are the heart of their communities, caring for young and old, providing love and nurture – as well as food and income. It is unacceptable that so many women die giving life, for lack of access to family planning, skilled midwifery and emergency obstetric care.

Join us

Our campaign, *Promise to Mothers Lost*, comes from and is inspired by those countries and communities where women are dying – and where men and women alike are speaking out, organizing and pressing for change.

We are targeting powerful global institutions and government officials, holding them to account through letter-writing campaigns, policymaker briefings, meetings, rallies, marches and forums, exhibitions of Stories of Mothers Lost and more.

For more information and to get involved, please visit:
www.promisetomothers.org

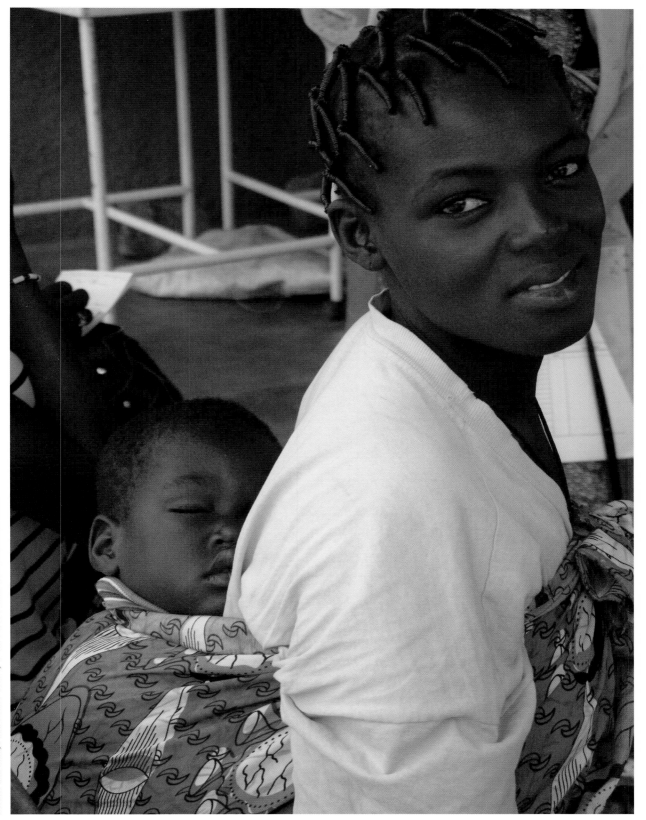

Mother and child, Fada Health Centre, White Ribbon Alliance Burkina Faso 2008

About the White Ribbon Alliance

The White Ribbon Alliance is an international coalition of organisations and individuals spanning 91 countries. Active from grassroots to government level, we work to save the lives of pregnant women and newborn children around the world.

The white ribbon is dedicated to the memory of all women who have died in pregnancy and childbirth. In some cultures, white symbolises mourning and in others it symbolises hope and life. The white ribbon represents this dual meaning globally. The White Ribbon Alliance not only works to sustain life and hope for all women, but also mourns and honours those women who did not survive pregnancy or childbirth.

To reduce maternal and newborn deaths and disabilities, the White Ribbon Alliance aims to:

Raise awareness around the world

Influence government policies

Mobilise communities

Empower local organisations

Share what works

Spark renewed action

Some of the successes since The White Ribbon Alliance began in 1999 include:

Policy changes
The White Ribbon Alliance of India successfully advocated for new regulations to allow auxiliary nurse-midwives to perform life-saving procedures.

More skilled health providers
The White Ribbon Alliance of Tanzania worked with the government to increase the number of available health workers.

Government commitment
The White Ribbon Alliance of Burkina Faso influenced political leaders to increase the budget for health.

Increased education and awareness
The White Ribbon Alliance of Indonesia organised nationwide 'Alert Villages,' for communities to recognise the danger signs in pregnancy and act quickly.

Amplified voices
White Ribbon Alliance Board members gave evidence to the influential 2008 United Kingdom Parliamentary Inquiry (International Development Committee) into maternal mortality – and its global solutions.

Improved transport
The White Ribbon Alliance of Malawi joined forces with the police and other partners to establish a fund for women's emergency transport to the hospital.

Men's involvement and support
The White Ribbon Alliance of India involves young husbands in childbirth education; they tie a white ribbon in the hair of their brides as a symbol of their commitment to their health and safety.

Holding leaders to account
By engaging with local communities and with the media, WRA members keep a 'social watch' to help women know their rights, to see if government policies are turned into action – and to check that quality services reach all women.

Working with government
The WRA not only proposes changes, but supports government efforts to provide equitable services to all citizens.

Media advocacy for mothers
All over the world, White Ribbon Alliance inspired films, television and radio programmes, newspaper and magazine articles tell our stories to the public and politicians.

Making connections and joining together
The White Ribbon Alliance around the world links its National Alliances, individual and organisational members to work together and share our resources to make pregnancy and childbirth safe for all women.

To become a member and learn more, visit www.whiteribbonalliance.org

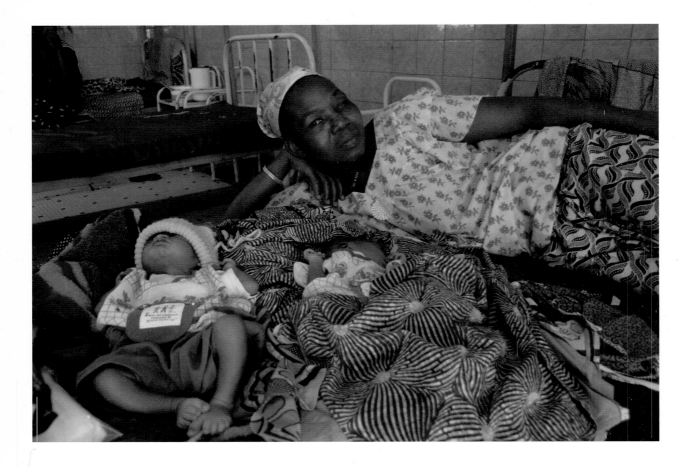

Acknowledgements

First and foremost, the White Ribbon Alliance would like to thank all of the members in every country who played their part in the creation and delivery of the fabric panels. Without their support and their dedication, no part of the *Stories of Mothers Lost* campaign would have been possible. In addition, the White Ribbon Alliance accords very special thanks for their tireless commitment to Betsy McCallon, Project Manager of *Stories of Mothers Lost* and the *Promise To Mothers Lost* campaign, and to Tamara Windau, our Senior Project Officer, and Deborah Clark, our Director of Communications in the US. Thanks are due also to the many White Ribbon Alliance supporters in the UK, in particular our patrons Sarah Brown, Anna Chancellor, Emma Freud and Diana Quick; to Claire Lewis for her wise advice and her time; to Maeve Shearlaw for her practical support; to Stuart Roden, whose generous donation made this book possible; to Maggie Darling, for her kindness in hosting its launch, and to the Royal College of Obstetricians and Gynaecologists International Office for their support of the London launch of the exhibit, especially Professor Jim Dornan, Beryl Stevens and Binta Patel.

The White Ribbon Alliance
For Safe Motherhood

CAN Mezzanine
32–36 Loman Street
London SE1 OEH
UK

Global Secretariat
One Thomas Circle NW, Suite 200
Washington DC 20005
USA

www.whiteribbonalliance.org